This book belongs to

....

....

Useful words

(in the order they appear in this book)

bath

bubbles

bridge

beakers

boats

banjo

baseball

breakfast

snowballs

buns

Bouncy Ben's
Bathtime

Susan Welby

Bouncy Ben thinks ...

baths are brilliant!

Bouncy Ben blows bubbles ...

in the bath.

Bouncy Ben builds bridges ...

in the bath.

Bouncy Ben balances beakers ...

in the bath.

Bouncy Ben sails boats ...

in the bath.

Bouncy Ben plays the banjo ...

in the bath.

Bouncy Ben plays baseball ...

in the bath.

Bouncy Ben makes breakfast ...

in the bath.

Bouncy Ben throws snowballs ...

in the bath.

Bouncy Ben makes buns ...

in the bath.

Bouncy Ben burrows ...

in the bath.

Bouncy Ben makes ...

a BIG mess in the bath!

The Letterlanders

Annie Apple	Bouncy Ben	Clever Cat	Dippy Duck	Eddy Elephant	Fireman Fred	Golden Girl

Hairy Hat Man	Impy Ink	Jumping Jim	Kicking King	Lucy Lamp Lady	Munching Mike

Naughty Nick	Oscar Orange	Poor Peter	Quarrelsome Queen	Robber Red	Sammy Snake	Ticking Tess

Uppy Umbrella	Vase of Violets	Wicked Water Witch	Max and Maxine	Yellow Yo-yo Man	Zig Zag Zebra

Published by Collins Educational
An imprint of HarperCollins*Publishers* Ltd
77-85 Fulham Palace Road
London W6 8JB

© Lyn Wendon 1998

First published 1998
Reprinted 1998

ISBN 0 00 303381 3

LETTERLAND® is a registered trademark of Lyn Wendon.

The author asserts the moral right to be identified as the author of
this work.

British Library Cataloguing in Publication Data
A catalogue record for this book is available from the British Library.

Written by Susan Welby
Illustrated by Anna Jupp
Designed by Michael Sturley and Sally Boothroyd
Consultant: Lyn Wendon, originator of Letterland

Printed by Printing Express Limited, Hong Kong

Letterland ™

Letterland At Home is a range of books, cassettes and flashcards that uses a fun approach to help children to read and write. Three colour-coded Stages will help you to choose the books that are right for your child.

Stage 1

MY FIRST Reading FLASHCARDS

MY FIRST Reading ACTIVITY BOOK — INCLUDES TWO PULL-OUT MASKS!

MY FIRST Handwriting ACTIVITY BOOK — INCLUDES WIPE-CLEAN ACTIVITY CARD!

MY FIRST Spelling ACTIVITY BOOK — ALL THE ALPHABET PLUS PULL-OUT JIGSAW!

Handwriting Songs

Alphabet Songs

Stage 2

MY SECOND Reading FLASHCARDS

MY SECOND Reading ACTIVITY BOOK — INCLUDES PULL-OUT READING GAME!

MY SECOND Handwriting ACTIVITY BOOK — INCLUDES WIPE-CLEAN ACTIVITY CARD!

MY SECOND Spelling ACTIVITY BOOK — INCLUDES PULL-OUT ACTIVITY CARD!

Available from all good bookshops.

For an information leaflet about Letterland call 0181 307 4052.

Stage 3

MY THIRD Reading FLASHCARDS

MY THIRD Reading ACTIVITY BOOK

MY THIRD Handwriting ACTIVITY BOOK

MY THIRD Spelling ACTIVITY BOOK

Letterland At Home

For younger children, a colourful range of first skills activity books has been developed.

Annie Apple's ART AND CRAFT BOOK

Bouncy Ben's BUSY BOOK

Clever Cat's COLOURING BOOK

Dippy Duck's DOT to DOT BOOK